Keys to Reading

Theodore L. Harris
Mildred Creekmore
Louise Matteoni

Harold B. Allen

Linguistic Consultant

Illustrated by Philip Smith

THE ECONOMY COMPANY
Oklahoma City   Indianapolis

Contents

Here We Are

Time for Pets

A Place to Play

Cover design by McRay Magleby
Cover illustration by Ron Eddington
Graphic Communications, Brigham Young University Press

ISBN 0–87892–422–1

On a City Street

Hill Farm

Fun for All

Acknowledgments

Grateful acknowledgment is given for permission to adapt and reprint the following copyrighted material:

"Down! Down!" Copyright, 1926, renewal, 1954 by Eleanor Farjeon. From the book *Poems for Children* by Eleanor Farjeon. Copyright, 1951, by Eleanor Farjeon. Reprinted by permission of J. B. Lippincott Company. Permission to reprint this poem has also been granted by David Higham Associates, Ltd. From *Silver-Sand and Snow* by Eleanor Farjeon; published by Michael Joseph.

"The Little Red Hen" from *Stories to Tell to Children* by Sara Cone Bryant. Adapted by permission of Houghton Mifflin Company.

"Mice" by Rose Fyleman, from *Fifty-One New Nursery Rhymes*, copyright 1932 by Doubleday & Company, Inc. Reprinted by permission of the publisher. Permission to reprint this poem has also been granted by The Society of Authors as the literary representative of the Estate of Rose Fyleman.

"Mossy" from "A Friend for a Tiny Turtle" by Frances B. Watts. Adapted by special permission from *Jack and Jill* Magazine © 1967 The Curtis Publishing Company.

"Sliding" from the book *Around and About* by Marchette Chute. Copyright 1946 by Marchette Chute. Published 1957 by E. P. Dutton & Co., Inc. and reprinted with their permission.

HERE WE ARE

how town owl low show

found our round four

grow loud gown pour cow

Sound the words.

now out

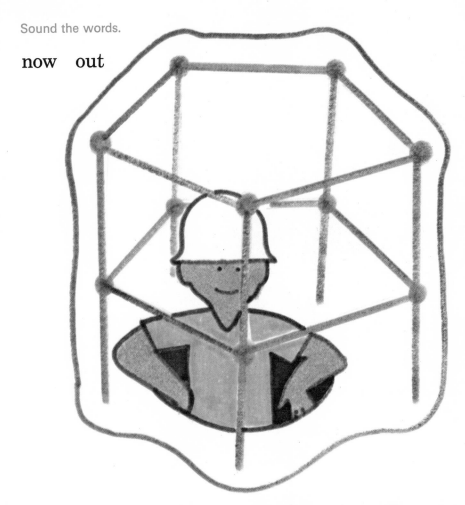

In and Out

L̶ook, Jan," said Ted.

"A man just went down that hole.
Let's wait for him to come out."

Jan said, "He may not come out now.
He has something to do.
Let's go and play ball now."

6

Jan hit the ball.

Ted ran to get it.

Then Jan ran, too.

But they didn't get the ball.

It went down the hole.

"Oh, no!" said Jan.

"We have to get the ball out."

Just then the man came out.
He came out with the ball.
"Is this your ball?" he said.

"Yes, it is," said Jan.

The man said, "I can't play now.
But here is your ball."
Then he went back down the hole.

broke broom flag flour

slow sleep slide stripe strap

try so fry

that's it's here's

Sound the words.

brown fly street what's

Sight word.

of

What's in the Box?

9

Don had a box with a lid.

"What's in your box?" Ted said.

"Something brown," said Don.
"Something that can hop and fly.
It can fly out of the box.
And it can hop to the street."

Kim said, "A plane can't hop.
But it can fly out of a box."

Jan said, "A frog can't fly.
But it can hop to the street."

"What's in the box?" Ted said.

"You can look now," said Don.

The lid came off the box.
Something brown came out.
It didn't stop!

"Oh, it can fly!" said Ted.
"It can fly out of the box.
It can hop to the street."

And off it went!

wall fall talk

shout shut shop slosh trash

feed loaf paint slide fruit

all walk made so

how show that's

A Good Game

Kim had no one to play with.
So she made up a game.

Then Jan came up the walk.
"What's that, Kim?" she said.

"That's a game," said Kim.
"We can play it on the walk."

"How do you play it?" Jan said.

"I will show you," said Kim.

Jan said, "Oh, I see how to play. That's a good game."

"Kim, may I play next?" said Gail.

"Kim, show me how to play,"
said Don.

Joe said, "Can't we all play?"

"Yes, show all of us," said Ted.

So Kim let all of them play.
She had made a good game
on the walk.

We work with words.

bird dirt curb hurt jerk
call odd fuss bell

Sound the words.

girl her Ann wall try

Sight words.

laugh won't

Try to Laugh

17

W̲ait for me, Sue," said Jan.

But Sue went on and did not wait
for her.

Jan sat down on the wall.

Then a girl came up to Jan.

But Jan did not see her.

"What's your name?"
said the girl.

Jan did not look at her.

"Won't you play with me?"
the girl said.

Now Jan did look at the girl.

"Sue won't wait for me,"
Jan said.

"She didn't want me to play
with her."

"Try to laugh," said the girl.

"We can have fun, too."

Jan did not laugh.
She did not try to laugh.

The girl sat down on the wall.
"What's your name?" she said.

Jan just sat still and did not tell
her name.

"My name is Ann," said the girl.

Now Jan did laugh.

She did not have to try.

"My name is Jan," she said
to the girl.

"Ann and Jan.

I like that.

That made me laugh."

sky skirt skate desk mask

cent cell mice place

ask skip race fall men

don't

What a Race!

23

Look at the men go!" Joe said.
"They hop, skip, and jump.
What a race!"

"I can race like that,"
Don said.
"I can hop, skip, and jump.
I can win a race like that."

24

Joe said, "Let's try to race
like that.
I will ask Ted, too.
Then we can all race."

Don and Joe went to ask Ted.

"Ted, did you see the race?"
said Joe.
"The men hop, skip, and jump.
We want to try it.
Will you race with us?"

"Don't ask me to race,"
Ted said.
"I didn't see the men.
I can't race like that."

"I will show you how to do it,"
Joe said.
"You just hop, skip, and jump.
I can do it.
Look at me go!"

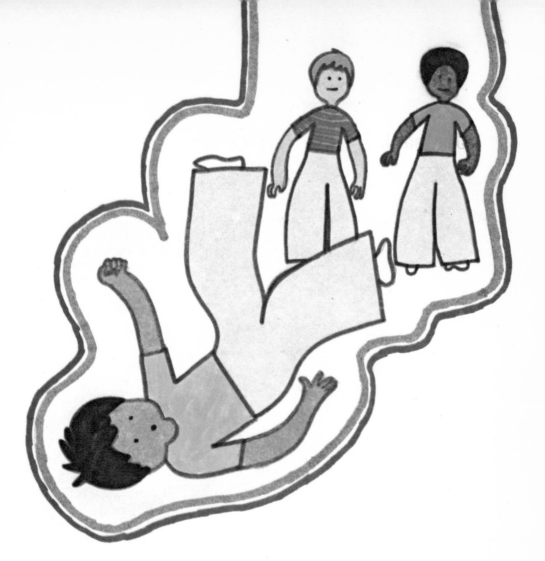

Joe went hop and skip.
But he did not jump.
Joe had a fall!

"What a race!" Ted said.
"Hop, skip, and fall down.
Don't ask me to race like that!"

TIME FOR PETS

jumps   looks   calls   plays

cats   pets   trees   pigs

fur   shirt   fern   turn

Sound the words.

dogs   girls   wants   bird

bad   I'll

Sight word.

where

Good Dog!

P ug wants something," said Gail.
"Can you tell what he wants?"

"Oh, he just wants to go
for a walk," said Jan.
"I'll take Pug, and you
take your cat."

So they all went down the street.

"Look, Pug," said Jan.
"I'll show you a bird."

"Yap, yap!" said Pug.
And he made the bird fly.

"Stop, Pug," said Jan.
"You are a bad dog.
Good dogs don't do that."

Just then a truck went by.

"Yap, yap!" said Pug,
and he ran at the truck.

"Come back, Pug," said Jan.
"Bad dogs do that.
Now be a good dog."

Gail said, "Did you see my cat?
I put him down,
but I didn't see where he went."

"Yap, yap!" said Pug.
And he ran to a tree.

Then the girls ran to the tree.
"Is that where the cat is?"

"Good dog, Pug!" said the girls.
"You are a good dog to show us
where the cat is."

toy joy oil boil point

say gray tray stray

boy way cats curb sad

friend

A Pet for a Boy

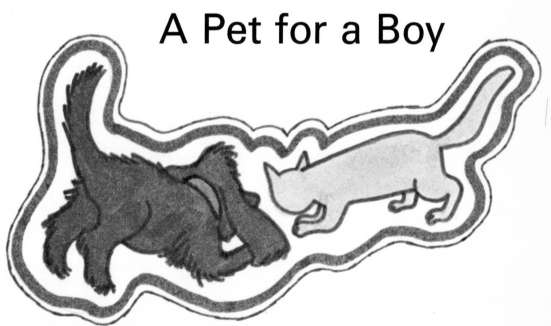

Jan ran with Pug.

But the boy just sat on the curb.

"She has fun with her dog,"
said the boy.

"Dogs are fun.

But I don't have one."

"Where is your dog?" Jan said.

"I don't have one," said the boy.

"Don't you like dogs?" Jan said.

"Yes," said the sad boy.
"But my father won't let me have one.
He said dogs are too big."

Jan sat on the curb
with her friend.
Then Bob came by.
He had his cat with him.

"Bob has fun with his cat,"
said the boy.
"Cats are fun.
But I don't have one."

Bob sat down on the curb, too.
"Do you like cats?" he said.

"Yes," said the sad boy.
"But my mother won't let me
have one.
She said cats get in the way."

Just then Pug ran at something
in the grass.
The cat ran at something, too.

"What's that?" the boy said.

"It is not too big," said Jan.

"And it won't get in the way,"
said Bob.

"I can put it in a box,"
the boy said with a laugh.
"Then I'll have a friend
to play with."

We work with words.

horn fork short storm

word worst world

ice lace rice bounce

Sound the words.

or work mice bell pets

Sight word.

school

Pets at School

43

This is the day for pets
at school," said Ted.
"I have a dog.
Gail has a cat.
And Joe has something in a box
with a lid on it."

44

"Do you want to work now?"
said Miss Bell.

"Or do you want to see the pets?"

"Let's show the pets," said Joe.

"I want you to see my pets now."

He got the lid off his box.
But then he said,
"Where are my pets?
They are not here!"

"What are they?" Miss Bell said.
"What are your pets?"

"Mice," said Joe.
"I had mice in the box."

"Oh, no!" said Miss Bell.
"We have to get the mice,
or no one will work."

"Here they are," said Gail.

"Sh," said Miss Bell.
"Be still."

Joe put the box down.
"Sh," he said. "Sh."

Then the mice ran to the box.
And Joe put the lid on.

"That's all the time we have
for pets now," said Miss Bell.
"Let's get to work."

Mice

I think mice
Are rather nice.

Their tails are long,
Their faces small,
They haven't any
Chins at all.
Their ears are pink,
Their teeth are white,
They run about
The house at night.
They nibble things
They shouldn't touch
And no one seems
To like them much.

But *I* think mice
Are nice.

Rose Fyleman

wash   wad   wand

boot   moon   book   foot   stood

was   soon   say   toy   word   talk

Blue Boy

Where is your pet?" Ted said.

"At home," said Ann.

"May I play with it?" Ted said.

"Oh, my pet can't come out,"
said Ann.

"And it can't play with you."

"Then what good is it?"
Ted said.

"It can talk to me," said Ann.

"A pet that can talk?" Ted said.
"You will have to show me that."

Soon Ann was home,
and Ted was with her.

"Now show me a pet that can talk,"
said Ted.

"Here he is," said Ann.
"Blue Boy, say something
to my friend."

The bird just sat still.

"Come on, Blue Boy," said Ann.
"Say a word for my friend."

The bird didn't say a word.
But soon he gave a hop,
and he got his feet wet.

"Look. He's all wet," said Ted.

"Oh, Blue Boy," said Ann.
"Be a good bird and say your
name for Ted."

The bird ran up and down a toy,
but he still didn't say a word.

With a laugh Ted said,
"He can fly.
He can get wet.
And he can play with a toy.
But that bird can't talk."

"Can't talk!" said the pet.
"Can't talk!"

raw   jaw   paw   yawn

night   light   sigh   bright

sled   slice   slow

Sound the words.

saw   high   boys   sleep

Pets

One day the boys went
to a pet show.

They saw pets play and eat
and sleep.

They saw dogs and cats and mice.

High on a wall they saw a bird.

And high on a stand they
saw a fish.

What pet in the show do you
like best?

The boys saw that the pets had
something good to eat.

They had something to sleep on.

And they had boys or girls to
pet them.

But the boys saw one pet that
you can't pet.

What was it?

A PLACE TO PLAY

We work with words.

car   far   arm   star   yard
hall   tall   stalk

Sound the words.

park   call   hurt   slide   top

Sight words.

two   again

Fun for Two

What can we do in the park?"
Ted said.

"Something two can play."

"Here is a slide in the park,"
said Jan.

"Two can play on the slide."

"Look at me, Ted," said Jan.
And up Jan went to the top
of the slide.
Then down she came.

"Look at me, Jan," said Ted.
Up Ted went to the top.
And down he came.

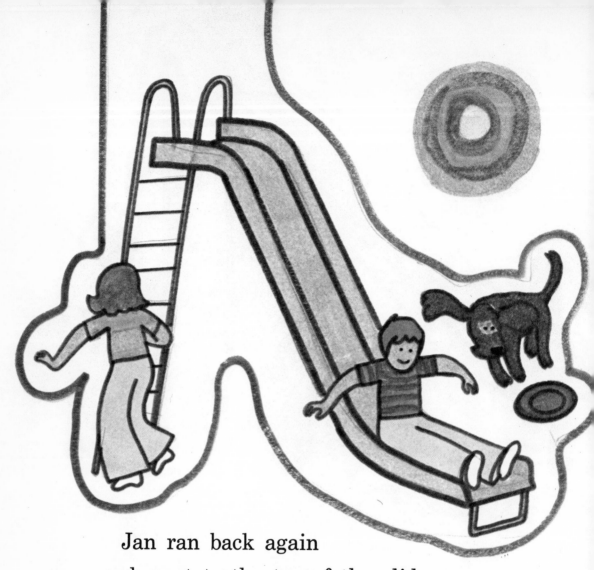

Jan ran back again
and went to the top of the slide.
Then down she came.

Ted ran back again.
But then he said, "Oh, no!
Pug is at the top of the slide.
We will have to call him."

"Come down, Pug," said Ted.
"You won't fall.
You won't get hurt."
But Pug did not come down.

"Go on, Pug," said Jan.

"It won't hurt you."

But still Pug did not go down.

"Call him again," said Ted.

"I see something
that will get Pug down," said Jan.

Jan made the toy fly.

Pug saw it go by.

So down he came.

Down, down the slide.

"Now two of us can play
on the slide again," said Jan.

And up she went to the top.

Sliding

Down the slide
  We ride, we ride.
Round we run, and then
  Up we pop
  To reach the top,
Down we come again.

Marchette Chute

We work with words.

yellow   letter   supper

apple   puzzle   bottle

parks   balls   ducks   walks

Sound the words.

rabbit   little   car   looks   trees

Sight words.

Mr.   into

A Walk in the Park

Jan and Sue went for a walk
in the park.

They saw Mr. Green at work.

They saw the big trees.

Then they saw something
by the big trees.

It was something little.

"What's that?" said Jan.

"It looks like a little toy," said Sue.

"No, it looks like a rabbit," said Jan.
"And that's what it is.
A little rabbit!"

Just then the rabbit saw
the two girls.

Hop, hop it went by the trees.

Then hop, hop it went
into the street.

"Oh, no," said Sue.

"Don't stop in the street,
little rabbit.

You will get hurt."

"Oh, look at that car!" said Jan.
"It will hit the rabbit.
What can we do?"

"I'll call Mr. Green," said Sue.
"He can help us."

Soon Mr. Green came.

He went into the street,
and he made the car stop.

Then hop, hop went the rabbit
out of the street.

And hop, hop it went
off into the trees.

We work with words.

penny   hobby   funny   silly
follow   bubble   waffle

Sound the words.

happy   yellow   am   seen   sun

Sight word.

pretty

Red, Yellow, and Brown

It was a pretty fall day.
The sun made the trees
look red, yellow, and brown.
But Kim was not happy.

"Where is it?" she said.
"I put it down and went
to play in the sun.
Now I don't see it."

Kim went up and down the park.
She still didn't see it,
but she saw a girl.

"Have you seen something
by a tree?" Kim said.

"No," said Jan.
"I was not by the trees.
I was in the sun."

So Kim went this way
and that way.

She still didn't see it,
but she saw a boy.

"Have you seen something yellow?"
said Kim.

"No," said Joe.
"I am on my way to play ball.
So I can't help you look."

Kim went on to this tree
and to that tree.
She still didn't see it,
but she saw a man.

"I am happy to help you look
for something," said Mr. Green.
"Did you put it by a tree?"

"Yes," said Kim.

"Is it yellow?" said Mr. Green.
"And is it a coat?"

"Yes, oh, yes," said Kim.

"Then just look for something
red, yellow, and brown," he said.

Kim was happy again.
With a laugh she said,
"Oh, look at my pretty coat.
It is red, yellow, and brown."

Down! Down!

Down, down!
Yellow and brown
The leaves are falling over the town.

Eleanor Farjeon

pony tiny table over

city robin

corn north worm worth

baby hello funny cut short

Mrs.

Make a Baby Laugh

Ted ran down the street.

He was on his way to play with Don.

"I want to be on time," said Ted.

"So I'll take a short cut.

I'll run by the park.

That's the best short cut

I can take."

"Hello, Mrs. Wall," said Ted.
"I came to play with Don."

"Hello, Ted," said Mrs. Wall.
"Don will be happy to see you.
He is with the baby.
Come in and see them."

"The baby can laugh," said Ted.
"I look funny to her.
I can make a baby laugh."

"My baby is happy,"
said Mrs. Wall.
"A happy baby
will laugh and laugh."

It made Ted happy
to see the baby laugh.
"I want a baby in my home,
too," said Ted.
"I like to be funny
and make a baby laugh."

think   bank   junk   pink   honk

horse   house   goose   nose   noise

third   those   thud   thirst

Sound the words.

thank   please   parks   place   rest

Parks

We all like to go to parks.

A park may be a little place.

It may have grass and trees and
a seat to rest on.

Or it may be a big place.

It may be so big that you can't
see it all in one day.

Parks have something in them
to please all of us.

You can play on a slide.

You can run a race or
fly a kite.

You may see a rabbit or a bird.
A boy can rest in the sun.
A girl can walk her dog.
A mother and father may come
to the park to please a baby.

Who can make the park pretty?
Can we thank them?
How can we thank them?
How can we help them make it
a good place for all of us?

ON A CITY STREET

We work with words.

called played waited

asked jumped

cider cabin paper

Sound the words.

looked wanted laughed

city far horse

Sight word.

there

There Is a Way

I like this city!" said Jan.

She looked down and saw
something little.

She looked far up and saw
something big.

Jan wanted to see the city.

She wanted to ride with the man
and his horse.

"I like this city, too!" said Ted.

He looked far down the street
at the boys.

Ted wanted to walk down
from the street.

He wanted to ride the train.

"I like this city," said Father.
He looked up and down the street.
He wanted to see
all there was to see.

"This is a big city," said Mother.
"We want to see all of it."

"It will take time to see
all of the city," said Father.
"We want to see the park.
And ride on the train down there."

"I want to go to a show," said Ted.

"I want to go on a boat ride,"
said Jan.

"There is a way!" Mother laughed.

"There is a way to see it all.

We will ride with the man
and his horse.

We will go to the park
and to a show.

And ride on the train and the boat.

We can do all that we want to do."

"But how can we?" said Jan.

"We will just go to one place
at a time," said Mother.

"And we won't try to do it
in just one day," laughed Father.
"That's the way we will see
this city."

chin   chalk   chicken   much

rang   thing   hung   bring

chase   string   tried   broke

balls   cars

helped   jumped

The Box of String

J an and Ted went out with Mother
and Father to see the city.

"I miss Pug," Ted said.

"But he didn't ride here
on the bus with us.

Dogs can't ride on a bus."

"It is good to have Pug
at home," said Father.

"He may just get in the way
and chase cars here."

Then they came to a curb.
A girl was there, too.
The girl had a box of string.

Just then the box broke!
Balls of string went this way
and that way.

Father tried to chase a ball
of string into the street.
But the girl said, "Look out!"
Father saw cars!
He jumped back.

Jan tried to chase a ball of string.
But it went into a hole.
A man said, "Get back!"
Jan jumped out of the way.

Jan and Father ran and jumped.
Ted and Mother went this way
and that.
No one helped them.
But one by one they got
the balls of string.

"I have to do something,"
said the girl.

"The box broke.

It is no good to me now."

"We can help," said Mother.

So the girl put the box down.

And they all put the
balls of string back into it.

Then they helped the girl put
string on the box.

"Thank you," said the girl.

"My box broke,

and you helped me."

Then she went up the street.

Mother looked at Father

and laughed.

"We came here to have

a good time," she said.

"Not to chase string.

But it was fun to help that girl."

bear   wear   ear   near

earn   learn

showed   worked   rested

hear   heard

asked   called   played

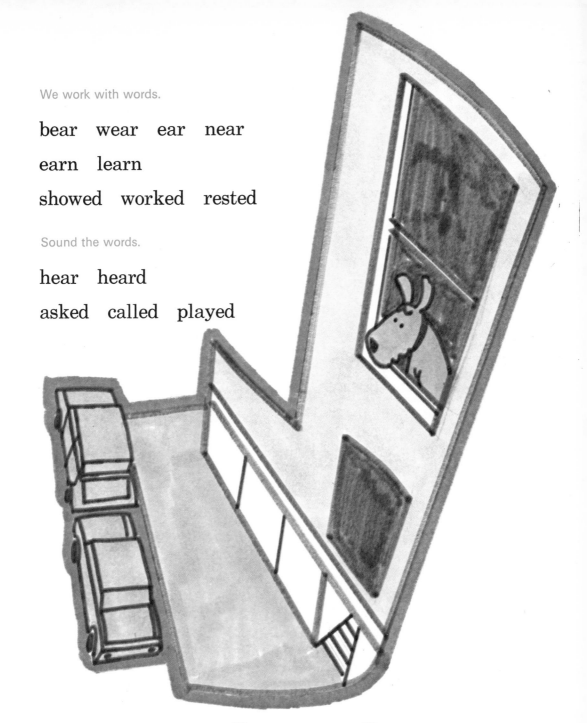

Street Game

Did you hear something?" asked Jan.

"I heard a dog," Ted said.
"But I don't see it."

Ted and Jan heard it again.
Then they looked up high
and saw it.

"Yap, yap," went the dog.
And it looked down at the street.

"What can the dog see?" Ted asked.
"What can it hear?
It wants something."

Jan looked down the street.
"Ted, look there!" she said.
"See the boys and girls?
That's what the dog heard.
The boys and girls will play ball."

Soon the boys and girls played.
A boy hit the ball.
The rest ran for it.

Boys and girls came to the curb.
They wanted to see the game.

"Hit the ball!" called
the boys and girls.

"Hit it!" they called.

And they jumped up and down
as the boys and girls played.

Ted jumped up and down, too.

"Run! Run!" he called.

Then he said, "I like this game."

"Yap, yap," went the little dog.
"Yap, yap, yap."

Jan heard the dog.
She looked up and laughed.
"Is this what you wanted?"
she asked the dog.
"Do you like the game, too?"

few   chew   mew   blew

blink   grain   plant   flash

new   block   gate

The Game Truck

The boys and girls saw a truck
come up the block.

There was a gate on the truck.

The gate was put up on the street.

It will not let cars in.

Now boys and girls can play
on this block.

What is in the truck?
Is it a new game?
No, the game is not new.
Boys and girls have played
this game at school.

This is not a new game,
but it is a new way to play.

Have you seen a gate like this?

Have you played on a block
like this?

Do you like the new way to play?

basket　party　turtle　circle

might　fright　sight

after　night　ate　last

our　it's

The Last Night

I t's our last night in this city,"
said Ted.

"And it had to rain!"

"Please make it quit, Father,"
laughed Jan.

"Then we can do something."

Father laughed, too.

"Don't try to be funny, Jan,"
said Ted.

"The rain made it a bad night."

So Jan ate, and she didn't
say a word.

After she ate her cake,
she went to look out.

She looked and looked.

Soon Mother said, "Ted,
go after Jan.

Tell her it's time to go."

Ted went after Jan.

But he looked out, and he
didn't come back.

He just looked and looked.

Soon Father said, "It's time
for us to go.

I'll have to get Ted and Jan."

He went after them.
But he looked out,
and he didn't come back.

At last Mother went after
all of them.
Then she looked out.

Jan said, "The block looks red.
The rain and the cars make it
look that way."

"And look at all the yellow
in the black wall," said Ted.
"Our last night here is not
so bad after all."

"No," said Mother.
"It's a pretty night in the city."

"And the rain made our last
night pretty," said Father.

HILL FARM

old told gold fold sold

clean cluck three threw

grow clown mouse round

barn party dark

Sound the words.

cold farm milk

throw cow found house

The Ride

Hello!" called Mrs. Hill
as she came out of the house.
 "At last you came to the farm."

 "Do you have a cow?" asked Pete.
 "May I ride it, please?"

Ted and Jan laughed.
Mrs. Hill laughed, too.

Then Mrs. Hill said,
"Yes, I have a cow.
 But come to the house now.
 I have cold milk for you."

116

Jan, Ted, and Pete
had good cold milk.

Then they went with Mrs. Hill
to see the cow.

They went a short way,
and then they found the cow.

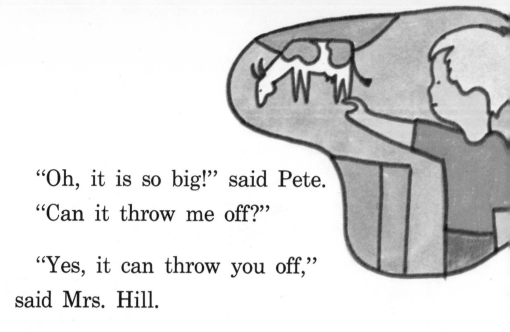

"Oh, it is so big!" said Pete.
"Can it throw me off?"

"Yes, it can throw you off,"
said Mrs. Hill.

At last Jan said,
"Oh, Pete, a cow will let you
have milk.
But a cow won't give you a ride."

On the way back to the house
Mrs. Hill found something for Pete.
"You can ride this," she said.

"This is fun," said Pete.
"And it won't throw me off."

alike   alone   asleep   around

candy   picnic   lazy   pupil

Sound the words.

about   away   pony   basket

barn   feed

Fun on the Pony

Pete, we can ride the pony,"
said Jan.

"Mrs. Hill said so."

"Oh, boy!" said Pete.
"It's in the barn.
Let's go!"

Away they went to the barn.
And soon Jan was on the pony.

Pete tried to get on the pony.
"It's too high," he said.
"Can I stand on that basket?"

"No, Pete, stand on that block.
The basket has a hole in it,"
said Jan.
And she helped him get on.

Then Pete said, "Get up, pony."
But the pony did not go.

"That basket may be in the way,"
said Jan.
"I'll take it away."

Jan jumped down.

Then she heard Pete call,
"Stop, pony!

Wait for Jan."

Jan got on the pony again.

"Now we can go," she said.

"Get up, pony."

The pony looked back
at Jan and Pete.

But it did not go.

Jan tried again.

"Get up, pony," she said.

"Please give us a ride."

But the pony just looked down.

"There is something funny
about this pony," said Jan.

"I'll get feed for the pony.

She may want feed."

After Jan got down, the pony
went out of the barn.

"Now I see what is funny
about the pony," said Jan.
"She didn't want me to ride.
The pony will ride one,
but she won't ride two."

So Pete went for a short ride.
He went out the gate and
up the hill.

Then Jan went for a ride.
She went down the hill and
back to the barn.

wheat   while   when   which

knee   knob   knock

flew   knew   joy   noise

white   know   fat   few   oil   pig

around   chicken   chickens

Around the Truck

Mother wanted to help
on the farm.

She asked Mrs. Hill, "Is there
something I can do?"

"Do you know how to put oil
in a truck?" asked Mrs. Hill.

"Yes, I can help you do that,"
said Mother.

"Let's get the truck
out of the sun," said Mrs. Hill.
"Hop in, Ted.
We will take it to the barn."

After they got to the barn,
they went to work.

Mother looked around the truck.

Soon she found the place to let
the oil out.

Ted wanted to see.

So he sat down on a basket.

"Don't get in the way, Ted,"
said Mrs. Hill.

"You will get oil on you."

"What about that chicken and
that pig?" said Ted.

"They are in the way."

"Yes, I know," said Mother.
"And they may get in the oil.
Chase them away, Ted."

The chicken ran away from Ted.
But the fat pig ran
around the truck.

Soon Mother cut a hole in a can
of oil.

"Now we can put in the new oil,"
she said.

But Ted didn't hear her.

He saw a few white chickens
come around the truck.

"Get away, chickens," said Ted.

Just then the fat pig ran
into Mother.

Mother looked down.

She saw a few white chickens.

She saw one white pig.

And she saw oil on all of them.

Ted laughed.
Mother and Mrs. Hill laughed.

"I know I have not helped you,
Mrs. Hill," said Mother.

"But now I have a few black and
white chickens," said Mrs. Hill.

"And you have one black and white
pig," said Ted.

looking   jumping   playing   throwing

cloud   club   throne   throat

eating   going   cluck   three

ducks   pigs

hen   peep   wee

At the Barn

Ted and Jan went out to the barn
at Hill Farm.

Mrs. Hill put out feed.

She wanted Ted and Jan
to see something.

Soon a white duck ran by.

"Quack, quack," it said.

Then one, two, three ducks
ran by.

They all went to the feed
and ate and ate.

Then a fat little pig ran by.

It was black and white.

The fat pig said, "Wee, wee!"
as he came in at the gate.

Then he went to the feed.

"Look," said Ted.

"Here are one, two, three
fat pigs.

They are all going to eat."

"I see a mother hen," said Jan.
"She has three baby chickens."

"Here they come," said Ted.
"They are going to eat, too.
See them run, Jan?"

"Cluck, cluck!" said the hen
as she ran by.
"Cluck, cluck!"

"Peep, peep, peep!"
said the three baby chickens.
"Peep, peep, peep!"

Ted and Jan saw the ducks eating.
They saw the pigs eating.
They saw the mother hen
and her baby chickens eating.

Then Ted and Jan saw Pug.
He ran in at the gate.

"Get away, Pug!" said Ted and Jan.
"Get away!
That feed is not for you."

"Yap, yap!" said Pug
as he ran at the chickens.
"Yap, yap! Yap, yap!" he said
as he ran at the pigs and ducks.

The ducks said, "Quack, quack!"
The pigs said, "Wee, wee!"
The mother hen said,
"Cluck, cluck! Cluck, cluck!"
The baby chickens said,
"Peep, peep, peep!"
And away they all ran
with Pug after them.

Ted and Jan ran, too.
They ran after Pug.
At last they got him.
Then they all went back
to the house.

bean leap head thread

great break

why wheel whip

wheat bread ready bake

loaf grow round

A Big Round Ball

Ted and Jan came in as Mrs. Hill
made a big round ball.

Jan looked all around it.

Then she asked, "What is it?"

"It's going to be bread,"
said Mrs. Hill.

And she hit the big round ball
again and again.

"Oh, my!" said Jan.

"I didn't know you made bread that way.

Won't that hurt the bread?"

Mrs. Hill laughed.

"Just wait," she said.

"After we bake it, you will see."

"Did you grow the wheat
for the bread?" Ted asked.

"Yes, I grow wheat on the farm,"
said Mrs. Hill.

"And my cow gave milk
for the bread."

Mrs. Hill made the bread all
round again.

"Now I'll put it where it
won't get cold," she said.

"Soon it will be ready to bake."

Jan and Ted didn't want to wait.
They wanted to see a loaf of bread.
But at last it was ready.

Mrs. Hill cut a loaf of bread.
She gave Jan and Ted bread
and cold milk.

They ate and ate.
Then they looked at Mrs. Hill.
"Oh, Mrs. Hill, you bake good
bread," Jan said.
"You didn't hurt it at all!"

FUN
FOR
ALL

142

loose   these   base   use   rose

lady   birthday   puddle   habit

flour   goose   grain   mill

plant   puppet   puppets

The Puppet Show

Ted, look at my puppets,"
said Jan.

"Let's play with them."

"What do you want to do
with the puppets?" asked Ted.

"Let's have a show," said Jan.
"Let's have a show for the boys
and girls we know."

"What will the show be about?"
asked Ted.

"It can be about
the Little Red Hen," said Jan.
"I want to be the hen and
the baby chickens."

"Then I will be the Goose
and the Duck," said Ted.

So Ted and Jan gave a puppet show.
They gave a show for the
boys and girls.
And this is what the show
was about.

The Little Red Hen

"I have found a grain of wheat,"
said the Little Red Hen.
"Who will help me plant
the grain of wheat?"

"Not I," said the Goose.

"Not I," said the Duck.

"Then I will plant it,"
said the Little Red Hen.
And she did.

At last the wheat was ready.
Then she said, "Who will take
the wheat to the mill?"

"Not I," said the Goose.

"Not I," said the Duck.

"Then I will," said
the Little Red Hen.
And she did.

Soon the Little Red Hen
came back from the mill.

She had the flour that was made
from the wheat.

"Who will bake a loaf of bread
from this flour?" she asked.

"Not I," said the Goose.

"Not I," said the Duck.

"Then I will bake the bread,"
said the Little Red Hen.

And she made a big loaf of bread.

After the bread was ready to eat,
she asked, "Who will eat the bread?"

"I will!" said the Goose.

"I will!" said the Duck.

"No, you won't,"
said the Little Red Hen.
"I will eat it.
Cluck, cluck! Cluck, cluck!"
She called to her baby chickens.
And the baby chickens came
to help her eat the loaf of bread.

"I like that show," said Joe.

"That's a good show,"
said Bob.

"May we come to your house
again?" asked Ann and Sue.

"Yes," said Ted and Jan.
"Come back and see a new
puppet show."

hold   chalk   wander   sky   ago

fuse   sink   knew   choice

old   mouse   why   slow

I'm   birds   turtle

The Race

I want to race, too," said Bob.
"But they won't let me.
They say I can't run
as fast as they can.
But I want to try."

Sue laughed and said,
"Come here, all of you.
Let me tell you about
a funny race."

One day Rabbit and Turtle
went for a walk.

Turtle was slow,
and Rabbit made fun of him.

"Turtle, why are you so slow?"
asked Rabbit.

"You can't run fast at all."

"I'm slow," said Turtle.

"But I get where I'm going."

Rabbit laughed at Turtle.

"I'm fast on my feet," he said.

"But you are funny and slow."

Now Turtle didn't like to be
laughed at.

So he said, "Let's run a race.
I'll show you who will win!"

"I'll win!" Rabbit said,
and he laughed again.

So Rabbit and Turtle got ready
for the race.

The old frog helped them.

And three birds and a mouse came
to see the race.

At last the old frog called,
"Get ready! Go!"

And off they went!

Soon Rabbit was far away.

"Turtle won't get this far,"
he said.

"So I'll sit here to rest."
And by and by he went to sleep.

But the turtle went on,
little by little.

And after a time he came
to the rabbit.

Turtle didn't stop to rest.
He just let Rabbit sleep.
The slow turtle went on,
little by little.
Then at last he came to a stop.

"You win!" called the old frog.
"You win!" called the birds
and the mouse.

Far away Rabbit heard them.
So he ran fast to see
what was going on.

"Rabbit, you can run fast,"
said the mouse.
"But you didn't win."

"Turtle is slow,"
said the birds.
"But he tried."

And the old frog said,
"Turtle didn't stop to rest.
So little by little he got here.
That's the way to win!"

"Oh, I get it, Sue," said Bob.
"I will run as fast as I can.
I can try to win the race!"

clear   early   pear   beard

wear   bed   cap   head   flew

paint   party   birthday

Paint, the Horse

Be still!" said Ted.
"It's time for the Paint show."

A few of the boys didn't hear.
So Ted called, "Are you ready?"

They heard a pop and a zip.
Then Don said, "Here it is!"

"Hello," said a horse.
"I'm Paint, the horse,
I am, I am.
I'm Paint, the horse, I am.

"I can't win a race.
I can't jump a wall.
From high in a place,
I head for a fall.

"I'm Paint, the horse,
I am, I am.
I'm Paint, the horse, I am."

Toy, the mouse, put a funny cap
on his head.
Cluck, the hen, put on a cap.
And so did Paint.
Then he got into bed.

Toy ran up the head of the bed.

"Why did you go to bed?"
he asked.

"I have my cap on," said Paint.
"I wear a cap in bed."

Cluck flew to the head
of the bed.

"That's not a cap to wear
in bed," she said.

"That's a cap to wear
to a party.

And we are going to have
a party."

"Yes, Paint, it's your birthday!"
said Toy.

"My bird day?" asked Paint
as he got out of bed.
"But I don't have a bird."

"Birthday!" laughed Cluck.
"This is your birthday party."

"Oh, my word!" said Paint.
"A birthday party!"
And he laughed a big party laugh.

"Here," said Cluck
as she gave Paint a box.

"A car!" said Paint.
"Thank you, Cluck.
You are a good old hen."

Then Paint sat on the car.
Pop! It broke!

"Why did you sit on it?"
asked Toy.
"It's just a little car."

"I wanted to ride," said Paint,
and he looked sad.

"Don't be sad," said Toy.
Then he gave Paint a top.

"Oh, thank you, Toy," said Paint.
"You are a good old mouse."
Then Paint made the top
jump and hop.
It flew around and around.

The horse laughed.
But the mouse ran to a basket,
and the hen flew out of the way.
They didn't want to get hurt.

Soon the top made one last hop.
It hit the wall, and it broke.

"Don't be sad, Paint," said Toy.
"The car and the top broke.
But here is a cake for you."

"A birthday cake!" said Paint.
He cut the cake, and they all
ate and ate.

At last Paint said,
"A happy horse, I am, I am.
I'm Paint, the horse, I am.
And happy birthday to me!"

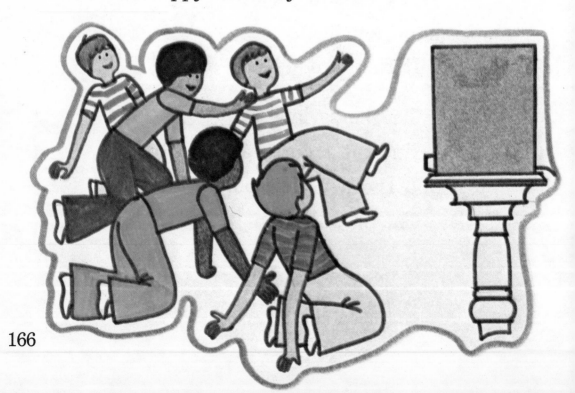

snap snow spot spin spell

heat breath steak meadow

snail spy leap sky over

tiny robin turtles

stroll Mossy

Fun for All

Father, Mother, and Ted
all sat around Jan.

"Are you ready?" Jan asked.
"You are going to hear about
a tiny turtle."

"We are ready," said Mother.
"Go on, Jan."

And this is what they heard.

Mossy

Mossy was a tiny turtle
who wanted to play.
But the big turtles
didn't want to play with him.
He was too little.

So one day Mossy went out
to look for a friend.
Soon he saw a robin
in a big tree.

"Will you be my friend?"
asked Mossy.

"Will you play with me?"

"Yes," said the robin.

"I'll be your friend.

I know a game we can play."

"What game?" asked Mossy.

"Sky-High, I Spy,"
said the robin.

"How do you play that game?"
asked Mossy.

"I fly up and hide in the sky,"
said the robin.

"Then you fly up and
look for me."

"A turtle can't fly up
to the sky," said Mossy.

"He can't fly at all."

"Then we can't play,"
said the robin.

And away she flew.

But Mossy didn't give up.
He still wanted a friend
to play with.

Soon he saw a fat frog.
"Hello, frog," said Mossy.
"Will you play with me?"

"Yes," said the frog.
"I'll play a game with you."

"What game?" asked Mossy.

"Leap and Jump," said the frog.

"How do you play that?"
asked Mossy.

"I leap and jump over you,"
said the frog.

"Then you leap and jump over me."

"But I can't leap and jump
over you," said Mossy.

"A turtle is slow.
He has to walk."

"Too bad," said the fat frog.
Then hop, hop, away he went.

Mossy was sad.

But he didn't give up.

He still went on.

At last the tiny turtle found
a little round snail.

"I'm Mossy," he said.

"Will you be my friend?

I want a friend to play with."

The snail looked sad.

"I can't play with you," he said.

"I can't fly, and I can't
jump or leap.

I will not be a good friend."

"Yes, you will," said Mossy.

"Turtles can't fly,
and they can't jump or leap.
So will you be my friend?"

"Yes," said the little round snail.

"What game can we play?"
asked Mossy.

"Slow—Slow—Stroll—About,"
said the snail.

This was a good game.
It was a good game
for a tiny turtle
and a little round snail.

"So at last Mossy found a friend
to play with," said Father.

"That was good, Jan," said Ted.

"Thank you," said Jan.

"Let's do this again,"
said Mother.
"Next time we will hear Ted."